Rick's Magic Stick

by Liza Charlesworth • illustrated by Richard Torrey

SCHOLASTIC INC.

New York • Toronto • London • Auckland • Sydney
Mexico City • New Delhi • Hong Kong • Buenos Aires

Designed by Grafica, Inc.
ISBN-13: 978-0-545-13781-2 • ISBN-10: 0-545-13781-0
Copyright © 2009 by Lefty's Editorial Services.
All rights reserved. Published by Scholastic Inc.
SCHOLASTIC, WORD FAMILY READERS™, and associated logos are trademarks and/or registered trademarks of Scholastic Inc.

12 11 10 9 8 7 6 5 4 3 2 1   9 10 11 12 13 14/0

Printed in the U.S.A.
First printing, September 2009

The Ick Family

What Is a Word Family?
A word family is a group of words that rhyme and share the same spelling pattern, such as *Rick, stick,* and *trick.* Read this story to learn more *–ick* words!

Meet **Rick**!
Rick is a member of the **Ick** family.

Rick has a mom, a dad,
and a brother named **Nick**.
He also has a magic **stick**.

One day, **Rick**
was doing a **trick** when…

OOPS!
Rick turned **Nick** into a **chick**!

"**Quick**! I must fix this!" said **Rick**.
So he waved his magic **stick**.

Now **Nick** was a **tick**!

"**Quick**! I must fix this!" said **Rick**.
So he waved his magic **stick**.

Now **Nick** was a **brick**!

Mr. and Mrs. **Ick** were worried **sick**.

Then **Rick** remembered to say the
magic words: "**Pick, wick, click**."

That did the **trick**!
Nick was **Nick**.

And that was the end of **Rick**'s
magic **stick**.

Word Family House

Point to the *-ick* word in each room and read it aloud.

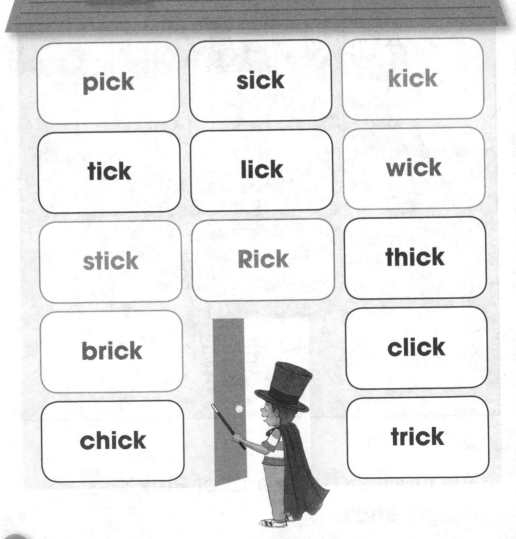

pick   sick   kick

tick   lick   wick

stick   Rick   thick

brick   click

chick   trick

Word Family Rhymes

Point to the rhyming pair that completes each sentence.

WORD BOX

chick flick

lick stick

sick tick

thick trick

quick pick

1 An ill bug is a _____ _____.

2 A movie for baby birds is a _____ _____.

3 A fast choice is a _____ _____.

4 A candy cane is a _____ _____.

5 A wide prank is a _____ _____.

Word Family Hunt

This hat has eight *-ick* words. Can you find them all? Cover them with pennies or buttons.